Sketches by S

(Volume 0

Robert Seymour

Alpha Editions

This edition published in 2023

ISBN : 9789357952668

Design and Setting By
Alpha Editions
www.alphaedis.com
Email - info@alphaedis.com

Contents

EVERYDAY SCENES.

SCENE I.

"Walked twenty miles over night: up before peep o' day again got a capital place; fell fast asleep; tide rose up to my knees; my hat was changed, my pockets picked, and a fish ran away with my hook; dreamt of being on a Polar expedition and having my toes frozen."

O! IZAAK WALTON!—Izaak Walton!—you have truly got me into a precious line, and I certainly deserve the rod for having, like a gudgeon, so greedily devoured the delusive bait, which you, so temptingly, threw out to catch the eye of my piscatorial inclination! I have read of right angles and obtuse angles, and, verily, begin to believe that there are also right anglers and obtuse anglers—and that I am really one of the latter class. But never more will I plant myself, like a weeping willow, upon the sedgy bank of stream or river. No!—on no account will I draw upon these banks again, with the melancholy prospect of no effects! The most 'capital place' will never tempt me to 'fish' again!

My best hat is gone: not the 'way of all beavers'—into the water—but to cover the cranium of the owner of this wretched 'tile;' and in vain shall I seek it; for 'this' and 'that' are now certainly as far as the 'poles' asunder.

My pockets, too, are picked! Yes—some clever 'artist' has drawn me while asleep!

My boots are filled with water, and my soles and heels are anything but lively or delighted. Never more will I impale ye, Gentles! on the word of a gentleman!—Henceforth, O! Hooks! I will be as dead to your attractions as if I were 'off the hooks!' and, in opposition to the maxim of Solomon, I will 'spare the rod.'

Instead of a basket of fish, lo! here's a pretty kettle of fish for the entertainment of my expectant friends—and sha'n't I be baited? as the hook said to the anger: and won't the club get up a Ballad on the occasion, and I, who have caught nothing, shall probably be made the subject of a 'catch!'

Slush! slush!—Squash! squash!

O! for a clean pair of stockings!—But, alack, what a tantalizing situation I am in!—There are osiers enough in the vicinity, but no hose to be had for love or money!

SCENE II.

A lark—early in the morning.

Two youths—and two guns appeared at early dawn in the suburbs. The youths were loaded with shooting paraphernalia and provisions, and their guns with the best Dartford gunpowder—they were also well primed for sport—and as polished as their gunbarrels, and both could boast a good 'stock' of impudence.

"Surely I heard the notes of a bird," cried one, looking up and down the street; "there it is again, by jingo!"

"It's a lark, I declare," asserted his brother sportsman.

"Lark or canary, it will be a lark if we can bring it down," replied his companion.

"Yonder it is, in that ere cage agin the wall."

"What a shame!" exclaimed the philanthropic youth,—"to imprison a warbler of the woodlands in a cage, is the very height of cruelty—liberty is the birthright of every Briton, and British bird! I would rather be shot than be confined all my life in such a narrow prison. What a mockery too is that piece of green turf, no bigger than a slop-basin. How it must aggravate the feelings of one accustomed to range the meadows."

"Miserable! I was once in a cage myself," said his chum.

"And what did they take you for?"

"Take me for?—for a 'lark.'"

"Pretty Dickey!"

"Yes, I assure you, it was all 'dickey' with me."

"And did you sing?"

"Didn't I? yes, i' faith I sang pretty small the next morning when they fined me, and let me out. An idea strikes me Suppose you climb up that post, and let out this poor bird, ey?"

"Excellent."

"And as you let him off, I'll let off my gun, and we'll see whether I can't 'bang' him in the race."

No sooner said than done: the post was quickly climbed—the door of the cage was thrown open, and the poor bird in an attempt at 'death or liberty,' met with the former.

Bang went the piece, and as soon as the curling smoke was dissipated, they sought for their prize, but in vain; the piece was discharged so close to the lark, that it was blown to atoms, and the feathers strewed the pavement.

"Bolt!" cried the freedom-giving youth, "or we shall have to pay for the lark."

"Very likely," replied the other, who had just picked up a few feathers, and a portion of the dissipated 'lark,'—"for look, if here ain't the—bill, never trust me."

SCENE III.

"You shall have the paper directly, Sir, but really the debates are so very interesting."

"Oh! pray don't hurry, Sir, it's only the scientific notices I care about."

WHAT a thrill of pleasure pervades the philanthropic breast on beholding the rapid march of Intellect! The lamp-lighter, but an insignificant 'link' in the vast chain of society, has now a chance of shining at the Mechanics', and may probably be the means of illuminating a whole parish.

Literature has become the favourite pursuit of all classes, and the postman is probably the only man who leaves letters for the vulgar pursuit of lucre! Even the vanity of servant-maids has undergone a change—they now study 'Cocker' and neglect their 'figures.'

But the dustman may be said, 'par excellence,' to bear—the bell!

In the retired nook of an obscure coffee-shop may frequently be observed a pair of these interesting individuals sipping their mocha, newspaper in hand, as fixed upon a column—as the statue of Napoleon in the Place Vendome, and watching the progress of the parliamentary bills, with as much interest as the farmer does the crows in his corn-field!

They talk of 'Peel,' and 'Hume,' and 'Stanley,' and bandy about their names as familiarly as if they were their particular acquaintances.

"What a dust the Irish Member kicked up in the House last night," remarks one.

"His speech was a heap o' rubbish," replied the other.

"And I've no doubt was all contracted for! For my part I was once a Reformer—but Rads and Whigs is so low, that I've turned Conservative."

"And so am I, for my Sal says as how it's so genteel!"

"Them other chaps after all on'y wants to throw dust in our eyes! But it's no go, they're no better than a parcel o' thimble riggers just making the pea come under what thimble they like,—and it's 'there it is,' and 'there it ain't,'—just as they please—making black white, and white black, just as suits 'em—but the liberty of the press—"

"What's the liberty of the press?"

"Why calling people what thinks different from 'em all sorts o' names— arn't that a liberty?"

"Ay, to be sure!—but it's time to cut—so down with the dust—and let's bolt!"

SCENE IV.

"Oh! Sally, I told my missus vot you said
your   missus   said   about   her."—

"Oh! and so did I, Betty; I told my missus vot
you said yourn said of her, and ve had sich a
row!"

SALLY. OH! Betty, ve had sich a row!—there vas never nothink like it;— I'm quite a martyr. To missus's pranks; for, 'twixt you and me, she's a bit of a tartar. I told her vord for vord everythink as you said, And I thought the poor voman vould ha' gone clean out of her head!

BETTY. Talk o' your missus! she's nothink to mine,—I on'y hope they von't meet, Or I'm conwinced they vill go to pulling of caps in the street: Sich kicking and skrieking there vas, as you never seed, And she vos so historical, it made my very heart bleed.

SALLY. Dear me! vell, its partic'lar strange people gives themselves sich airs, And troubles themselves so much 'bout other people's affairs; For my part, I can't guess, if I died this werry minute, Vot's the use o' this fuss—I can't see no reason in it.

BETTY. Missus says as how she's too orrystocratic to mind wulgar people's tattle, And looks upon some people as little better nor cattle.

SALLY. And my missus says no vonder, as yourn can sport sich a dress, For ven some people's husbands is vite-vashed, their purses ain't less; This I will say, thof she puts herself in wiolent rages, She's not at all stingy in respect of her sarvant's wages.

BETTY. Ah! you've got the luck of it—for my missus is as mean as she's proud; On'y eight pound a-year, and no tea and sugar allowed. And then there's seven children to do for—two is down with the measles, And t'others, poor things! is half starved, and as thin as weazles; And then missus sells all the kitchen stuff!—(you don't know my trials!) And takes all the money I get at the rag-shop for the vials!

SALLY. Vell! I could'nt stand that!—If I was you, I'd soon give her warning.

BETTY. She's saved me the trouble, by giving me notice this morning. But—hush! I hear master bawling out for his shaving water— Jist tell your missus from me, mine's everythink as she thought her!

SCENE V.

*"How does it fit behind? O! beautful; I've
done wonders—we'll never trouble the tailors
again, I promise them."*

IT is the proud boast of some men that they have 'got a wrinkle.' How
elated then ought this individual to be who has got so many! and yet,
judging from the fretful expression of his physiognomy, one would
suppose that he is by no means in 'fit' of good humour.

His industrious rib, however, appears quite delighted with her
handiwork, and in no humour to find the least fault with the loose habits of
her husband. He certainly looks angry, as a man naturally will when his
'collar' is up.

She, on the other hand, preserves her equanimity in spite of his
unexpected frowns, knowing from experience that those who sow do not
always reap; and she has reason to be gratified, for every beholder will agree

in her firm opinion, that even that inimitable ninth of ninths—Stulz, never made such a coat!

In point of economy, we must allow some objections may be made to the extravagant waist, while the cuffs she has bestowed on him may probably be a fair return (with interest) of buffets formerly received.

The tail (in two parts) is really as amusing as any 'tale' that ever emanated from a female hand. There is a moral melancholy about it that is inexpressibly interesting, like two lovers intended for each other, and that some untoward circumstance has separated; they are 'parted,' and yet are still 'attached,' and it is evident that one seems 'too long' for the other.

The 'goose' generally finishes the labours of the tailor. Now, some carping critics may be wicked enough to insinuate that this garb too was finished by a goose! The worst fate I can wish to such malignant scoffers is a complete dressing from this worthy dame; and if she does not make the wisest of them look ridiculous, then, and not till then, will I abjure my faith in her art of cutting!

And proud ought that man to be of such a wife; for never was mortal 'suited' so before!

SCENE VI.

"Catching—a cold."

WHAT a type of true philosophy and courage is this Waltonian!

Cool and unmoved he receives the sharp blows of the blustering wind—as if he were playing dummy to an experienced pugilist.

Although he would undoubtedly prefer the blast with the chill off, he is so warm an enthusiast, in the pursuit of his sport, that he looks with contempt upon the rude and vulgar sport of the elements. He really angles for love—and love alone—and limbs and body are literally transformed to a series of angles!

Bent and sharp as his own hook, he watches his smooth float in the rough, but finds, alas! that it dances to no tune.

Time and bait are both lost in the vain attempt: patiently he rebaits, until he finds the rebait brings his box of gentles to a discount; and then, in no gentle humour, with a baitless hook, and abated ardor, he winds up his line and his day's amusement(?)—and departs, with the determination of trying fortune (who has tried him) on some, future and more propitious day.

Probably, on the next occasion, he may be gratified with the sight of, at least, one gudgeon, should the surface of the river prove glassy smooth and mirror-like. (We are sure his self-love will not be offended at the reflection!) and even now he may, with truth, aver, that although he caught nothing, he, at least, took the best perch in the undulating stream!

SCENE VII.

"Help! help! Oh! you murderous little villin?
this is vot you calls rowing, is it?—but if ever I
gets safe on land again, I'll make you repent it,
you rascal. I'll row you—that I will."

"MISTER Vaterman, vot's your fare for taking me across?"

"Across, young 'ooman? vy, you looks so good-tempered, I'll pull you over for sixpence?"

"Are them seats clean?"

"O! ker-vite:—I've just swabb'd 'em down."

"And werry comfortable that'll be! vy, it'll vet my best silk?"

"Vatered silks is all the go. Vel! vell! if you don't like; it, there's my jacket. There, sit down a-top of it, and let me put my arm round you."

"Fellow!"

"The arm of my jacket I mean; there's no harm in that, you know."

"Is it quite safe? How the wind blows!"

"Lord! how timorsome you be! vy, the vind never did nothin' else since I know'd it"

"O! O! how it tumbles! dearee me!"

"Sit still! for ve are just now in the current, and if so be you go over here, it'll play old gooseberry with you, I tell you."

"Is it werry deep?"

"Deep as a lawyer."

"O! I really feel all over"—

"And, by Gog, you'll be all over presently—don't lay your hand on my scull"

"You villin, I never so much as touched your scull. You put me up."

"I must put you down. I tell you what it is, young 'ooman, if you vant to go on, you must sit still; if you keep moving, you'll stay where you are— that's all! There, by Gosh! we're in for it." At this point of the interesting dialogue, the young 'ooman gave a sudden lurch to larboard, and turned the boat completely over. The boatman, blowing like a porpoise, soon strode across the upturned bark, and turning round, beheld the drenched "fare" clinging to the stern.

"O! you partic'lar fool!" exclaimed the waterman. "Ay, hold on a-stern, and the devil take the hindmost, say I!"

SCENE VIII.

In for it, or Trying the middle.

A little fat man
With rod, basket, and can,
And tackle complete,
Selected a seat
On the branch of a wide-spreading tree,
That stretch'd over a branch of the Lea:
There he silently sat,
Watching his float—like a tortoise-shell cat,
That hath scented a mouse,
In the nook of a room in a plentiful house.
But alack!
He hadn't sat long—when a crack
At his back
Made him turn round and pale—
And catch hold of his tail!
But oh! 'twas in vain
That he tried to regain
The trunk of the treacherous tree;

So he
With a shake of his head
Despairingly said—
"In for it,—ecod!"
And away went his rod,
And his best beaver hat,
Untiling his roof!
But he cared not for that,
For it happened to be a superb water proof,
Which not being himself,
The poor elf!
Felt a world of alarm
As the arm
Most gracefully bow'd to the stream,
As if a respect it would show it,
Tho' so much below it!
No presence of mind he dissembled,
But as the branch shook so he trembled,
And the case was no longer a riddle
Or joke;
For the branch snapp'd and broke;
And altho'
The angler cried "Its no go!"
He was presently—'trying the middle.'

SEYMOUR'S SKETCHES

A DAY'S SPORT

"Arena virumque cano."

CHAPTER I.

*The   Invitation—the   Outfit—and   the
sallying forth.*

TO Mr. AUGUSTUS SPRIGGS,

AT Mr. WILLIAMS'S, GROCER, ADDLE STREET.

(Tower Street, 31st August, 18__)

My dear Chum,

Dobbs has give me a whole holiday, and it's my intention to take the field to-morrow—and if so be you can come over your governor, and cut the apron and sleeves for a day—why

"Together we will range the fields;"

and if we don't have some prime sport, my name's not Dick, that's all.

I've bought powder and shot, and my cousin which is Shopman to my Uncle at the corner, have lent me a couple of guns that has been 'popp'd.' Don't mind the expense, for I've shot enough for both. Let me know by Jim if you can cut your stick as early as nine, as I mean to have a lift by the Highgate what starts from the Bank.

Mind, I won't take no refusal—so pitch it strong to the old 'un, and carry your resolution nem. con.

And believe me to be, your old Crony,

RICHARD GRUBB.

P. S. The guns hasn't got them thingummy 'caps,' but that's no matter, for cousin says them cocks won't always fight: while them as he has lent is reg'lar good—and never misses fire nor fires amiss.

In reply to this elegant epistle, Mr. Richard Grubb was favoured with a line from Mr. Augustus Spriggs, expressive of his unbounded delight in having prevailed upon his governor to 'let him out;' and concluding with a promise of meeting the coach at Moorgate.

At the appointed hour, Mr. Richard Grubb, 'armed at all points,' mounted the stage—his hat cocked knowingly over his right eye—his gun half-cocked and slung over his shoulder, and a real penny Cuba in his mouth.

"A fine mornin' for sport," remarked Mr. Richard Grubb to his fellow-passenger, a stout gentleman between fifty and sixty years of age, with a choleric physiognomy and a fierce-looking pigtail.

"I dessay—"

"Do you hang out at Highgate?" continued the sportsman.

"Hang out?"

"Ay, are you a hinhabitant?"

"To be sure I am."

"Is there any birds thereabouts?"

"Plenty o' geese," sharply replied the old gentleman.

"Ha! ha! werry good!—but I means game;—partridges and them sort o' birds."

"I never see any except what I've brought down."

"I on'y vish I may bring down all I see, that's all," chuckled the joyous Mr. Grubb.

"What's the matter?"

"I don't at all like that 'ere gun."

"Lor! bless you, how timorsome you are, 'tain't loaded."

"Loaded or not loaded, it's werry unpleasant to ride with that gun o' yours looking into one's ear so."

"Vell, don't be afeard, I'll twist it over t'other shoulder,—there! but a gun ain't a coach, you know, vich goes off whether it's loaded or not. Hollo! Spriggs! here you are, my boy, lord! how you are figg'd out—didn't know you—jump up!"

"Vere's my instrument o' destruction?" enquired the lively Augustus, when he had succeeded in mounting to his seat.

"Stow'd him in the boot!"

The coachman mounted and drove off; the sportsmen chatting and laughing as they passed through 'merry Islington.'

"Von't ve keep the game alive!" exclaimed Spriggs, slapping his friend upon the back.

"I dessay you will," remarked the caustic old boy with the pigtail; "for it's little you'll kill, young gentlemen, and that's my belief!"

"On'y let's put 'em up, and see if we don't knock 'em down, as cleverly as Mister Robins does his lots," replied Spriggs, laughing at his own wit.

Arrived at Highgate, the old gentleman, with a step-fatherly anxiety, bade them take care of the 'spring-guns' in their perambulations.

"Thankee, old boy," said Spriggs, "but we ain't so green as not to know that spring guns, like spring radishes, go off long afore Autumn, you know!"

CHAPTER II.

The Death of a little Pig, which proves a great Bore!

"Now let's load and prime—and make ready," said Mr. Richard, when they had entered an extensive meadow, "and—I say—vot are you about? Don't put the shot in afore the powder, you gaby!"

Having charged, they shouldered their pieces and waded through the tall grass.

"O! crikey!—there's a heap o' birds," exclaimed Spriggs, looking up at a flight of alarmed sparrows. "Shall I bring 'em down?"

"I vish you could! I'd have a shot at 'em," replied Mr. Grubb, "but they're too high for us, as the alderman said ven they brought him a couple o' partridges vot had been kept overlong!"

"My eye! if there ain't a summat a moving in that 'ere grass yonder—cock your eye!" "Cock your gun—and be quiet," said Mr. Grubb. The anxiety of the two sportsmen was immense. "It's an hare—depend on't— stoop down—pint your gun,—and when I say fire—fire! there it is—fire!"

Bang! bang! went the two guns, and a piercing squeak followed the report.

"Ve've tickled him," exclaimed Spriggs, as they ran to pick up the spoil.

"Ve've pickled him, rayther," cried Grubbs, "for by gosh it's a piggy!"

"Hallo! you chaps, vot are you arter?" inquired a man, popping his head over the intervening hedge. "Vy, I'm blessed if you ain't shot von o' Stubbs's pigs." And leaping the hedge he took the 'pork' in his arms, while the sportsmen who had used their arms so destructively now took to their legs for security. But ignorance of the locality led them into the midst of a village, and the stentorian shouts of the pig-bearer soon bringing a multitude at their heels, Mr. Richard Grubb was arrested in his flight. Seized fast by the collar, in the grasp of the butcher and constable of the place, all escape was vain. Spriggs kept a respectful distance.

"Now my fine fellow," cried he, brandishing his staff, "you 'ither pays for that 'ere pig, or ve'll fix you in the cage."

Now the said cage not being a bird-cage, Mr. Richard Grubb could see no prospect of sport in it, and therefore fearfully demanded the price of the sucking innocent, declaring his readiness to 'shell out.'

Mr. Stubbs, the owner, stepped forward, and valued it at eighteen shillings.

"Vot! eighteen shillings for that 'ere little pig!" exclaimed the astounded sportsman. "Vy I could buy it in town for seven any day."

But Mr. Stubbs was obdurate, and declared that he would not 'bate a farden,' and seeing no remedy, Mr. Richard Grubb was compelled to 'melt a sovereign,' complaining loudly of the difference between country-fed and town pork!

Shouldering his gun, he joined his companion in arms, amid the jibes and jeers of the grinning rustics.

"Vell, I'm blowed if that ain't a cooler!" said he.

"Never mind, ve've made a hit at any rate," said the consoling Spriggs, "and ve've tried our metal."

"Yes, it's tried my metal preciously—changed a suv'rin to two bob! by jingo!"

"Let's turn Jews," said Spriggs, "and make a vow never to touch pork again!"

"Vot's the use o' that?"

"Vy, we shall save our bacon in future, to be sure," replied Spriggs, laughing, and Grubb joining in his merriment, they began to look about them, not for fresh pork, but for fresh game.

"No more shooting in the grass, mind!" said Grubb, "or ve shall have the blades upon us agin for another grunter p'r'aps. Our next haim must be at birds on the ving! No more forking out. Shooting a pig ain't no lark— that's poz!"

CHAPTER III.

The Sportsmen trespass on an Enclosure—
Grubb gets on a paling and runs a risk of being
impaled.

"Twig them trees?"—said Grubb.

"Prime!" exclaimed Spriggs, "and vith their leaves ve'll have an hunt there.—Don't you hear the birds a crying 'sveet,' 'sveet?' Thof all birds belong to the Temperance Society by natur', everybody knows as they're partic'larly fond of a little s'rub!"

"Think ve could leap the ditch?" said Mr. Richard, regarding with a longing look the tall trees and the thick underwood.

"Lauk! I'll over it in a jiffy," replied the elastic Mr. Spriggs there ain't no obelisk a sportsman can't overcome"—and no sooner had be uttered these encouraging words, than he made a spring, and came 'close-legged' upon the opposite bank; unfortunately, however, he lost his balance, and fell plump upon a huge stinging nettle, which would have been a treat to any donkey in the kingdom!

"Oh!—cuss the thing!" shrieked Mr. Spriggs, losing his equanimity with his equilibrium.

"Don't be in a passion, Spriggs," said Grubb, laughing.

"Me in a passion?—I'm not in a passion—I'm on'y—on'y—nettled!" replied he, recovering his legs and his good humour. Mr. Grubb, taking warning by his friend's slip, cautiously looked out for a narrower part of the ditch, and executed the saltatory transit with all the agility of a poodle.

They soon penetrated the thicket, and a bird hopped so near them, that they could not avoid hitting it.—Grubb fired, and Sprigg's gun echoed the report.

"Ve've done him!" cried Spriggs.

"Ve!—me, if you please."

"Vell—no matter," replied his chum, "you shot a bird, and I shot too!—Vot's that?—my heye, I hear a voice a hollering like winkin; bolt!"

Away scampered Spriggs, and off ran Grubb, never stopping till he reached a high paling, which, hastily climbing, he found himself literally upon tenter-hooks.

"There's a man a coming, old fellow," said an urchin, grinning.

"A man coming! vich vay? do tell me vich vay?" supplicated the sportsman. The little rogue, however, only stuck his thumb against his snub nose—winked, and ran off.

But Mr. Grubb was not long held in suspense; a volley of inelegant phrases saluted his ears, while the thong of a hunting-whip twisted playfully about his leg. Finding the play unequal, he wisely gave up the game—by dropping his bird on one side, and himself on the other; at the same time reluctantly leaving a portion of his nether garment behind him.

"Here you are!" cried his affectionate friend,—picking him up—"ain't you cotch'd it finely?"

"Ain't I, that's all?" said the almost breathless Mr. Grubb, "I'm almost dead."

"Dead!—nonsense—to be sure, you may say as how you're off the hooks! and precious glad you ought to be."

"Gracious me! Spriggs, don't joke; it might ha' bin werry serious," said Mr. Grubb, with a most melancholy shake of the head:—"Do let's get out o' this wile place."

"Vy, vat the dickins!" exclaimed Spriggs, "you ain't sewed up yet, are you?"

"No," replied Grubb, forcing a smile in spite of himself, "I vish I vos, Spriggs; for I 've got a terrible rent here!" delicately indicating the position of the fracture.

And hereupon the two friends resolving to make no further attempt at bush-ranging, made as precipitate a retreat as the tangled nature of the preserve permitted.

CHAPTER IV.

Shooting a Bird, and putting Shot into a Calf!

"ON'Y think ven ve thought o' getting into a preserve—that ve got into a pickle," said Sprigg, still chuckling over their last adventure.

"Hush!" cried Grubb, laying his hand upon his arm—"see that bird hopping there?"

"Ve'll soon make him hop the twig, and no mistake," remarked Spriggs.

"There he goes into the 'edge to get his dinner, I s'pose."

"Looking for a 'edge-stake, I dare say," said the facetious Spriggs.

"Now for it!" cried Grubb! "pitch into him!" and drawing his trigger he accidentally knocked off the bird, while Spriggs discharged the contents of his gun through the hedge.

"Hit summat at last!" exclaimed the delighted Grubb, scampering towards the thorny barrier, and clambering up, he peeped into an adjoining garden.

"Will you have the goodness to hand me that little bird I've just shot off your 'edge," said he to a gardener, who was leaning on his spade and holding his right leg in his hand.

"You fool," cried the horticulturist, "you've done a precious job— You've shot me right in the leg—O dear! O dear! how it pains!"

"I'm werry sorry—take the bird for your pains," replied Grubb, and apprehending another pig in a poke, he bobbed down and retreated as fast as his legs could carry him.

"Vot's frightened you?" demanded Spriggs, trotting off beside his chum, "You ain't done nothing, have you?"

"On'y shot a man, that's all."

"The devil!"

"It's true—and there'll be the devil to pay if ve're cotched, I can tell you—'Vy the gardener vill swear as it's a reg'lar plant!—and there von't be no damages at all, if so be he says he can't do no work, and is obleeged to keep his bed—so mizzle!" With the imaginary noises of a hot pursuit at their heels, they leaped hedge, ditch, and style without daring to cast a look behind them—and it was not until they had put two good miles of cultivated land between them and the spot of their unfortunate exploit that they ventured to wheel about and breathe again.

"Vell, if this 'ere ain't a rum go!"—said Spriggs—"in four shots—ve've killed a pig—knocked the life out o' one dicky-bird—and put a whole charge into a calf. Vy, if ve go on at this rate we shall certainly be taken up and get a setting down in the twinkling of a bed-post!"

"See if I haim at any think agin but vot's sitting on a rail or a post"—said Mr. Richard—"or s'pose Spriggs you goes on von side of an 'edge and me on t'other—and ve'll get the game between us—and then—"

"Thankye for me, Dick," interrupted Spriggs, "but that'll be a sort o' cross-fire that I sha'n't relish no how.—Vy it'll be just for all the world like fighting a jewel—on'y ve shall exchange shots—p'r'aps vithout any manner o' satisfaction to 'ither on' us. No—no—let's shoot beside von another— for if ve're beside ourselves ve may commit suicide."

"My vig!" cries Mr. Grubb, "there's a covey on 'em."

"Vere?"

"There!"

"Charge 'em, my lad."

"Stop! fust charge our pieces."

Having performed this preliminary act, the sportsmen crouched in a dry ditch and crawled stealthily along in order to approach the tempting covey as near as possible.

Up flew the birds, and with trembling hands they simultaneously touched the triggers.

"Ve've nicked some on 'em."

"Dead as nits," said Spriggs.

"Don't be in an hurry now," said the cautious Mr. Grubb, "ve don't know for certain yet, vot ve hav'n't hit."

"It can't be nothin' but a balloon then," replied Spriggs, "for ve on'y fired in the hair I'll take my 'davy."

Turning to the right and the left and observing nothing, they boldly advanced in order to appropriate the spoil.

"Here's feathers at any rate," said Spriggs, "ve've blown him to shivers, by jingo!"

"And here's a bird! hooray!" cried the delighted Grubb—"and look'ee, here's another—two whole 'uns—and all them remnants going for nothing as the linen-drapers has it!"

"Vot are they, Dick?" inquired Spriggs, whose ornithological knowledge was limited to domestic poultry; "sich voppers ain't robins or sparrers, I take it."

"Vy!" said the dubious Mr. Richard-resting on his gun and throwing one leg negligently over the other—"I do think they're plovers, or larks, or summat of that kind."

"Vot's in a name; the thing ve call a duck by any other name vould heat as vell!" declaimed Spriggs, parodying the immortal Shakspeare.

"Talking o' heating, Spriggs—I'm rayther peckish—my stomick's bin a-crying cupboard for a hour past.—Let's look hout for a hinn!"

CHAPTER V.

An extraordinary Occurrence—a Publican taking Orders.

TYING the legs of the birds together with a piece of string, Spriggs proudly carried them along, dangling at his fingers' ends.

After tramping for a long mile, the friends at length discovered, what they termed, an house of "hentertainment."

Entering a parlour, with a clean, sanded floor, (prettily herring-boned, as the housemaids technically phrase it,) furnished with red curtains, half a dozen beech chairs, three cast-iron spittoons, and a beer-bleached mahogany table,—Spriggs tugged at the bell. The host, with a rotund, smiling face, his nose, like Bardolph's, blazing with fiery meteors, and a short, white apron, concealing his unmentionables, quickly answered the tintinabulary summons.

"Landlord," said Spriggs, who had seated himself in a chair, while Mr. Richard was adjusting his starched collar at the window;—"Landlord! ve should like to have this 'ere game dressed."

The Landlord eyed the 'game' through his spectacles, and smiled.

"Roasted, or biled, Sir?" demanded he.

"Biled?—no:—roasted, to be sure!" replied Spriggs, amazed at his pretended obtuseness: "and, I say, landlord, you can let us have plenty o' nice wedgetables."

"Greens?" said the host;—but whether alluding to the verdant character of his guests, or merely making a polite inquiry as to the article they desired, it was impossible, from his tone and manner, to divine.

"Greens!" echoed Spriggs, indignantly; "no:—peas and 'taters."

"Directly, Sir," replied the landlord; and taking charge of the two leetle birds, he departed, to prepare them for the table.

"Vot a rum cove that 'ere is," said Grubb.

"Double stout, eh?" said Spriggs, and then they both fell to a-laughing; "and certain it is, that, although the artist has only given us a draught of the landlord, he was a subject sufficient for a butt!

"Vell! I must, say," said Grubb, stretching his weary legs under the mahogany, "I never did spend sich a pleasant day afore—never!"

"Nor I," chimed in Spriggs, "and many a day ven I'm a chopping up the 'lump' shall I think on it. It's ralely bin a hout and houter! Lauk! how Suke vill open her heyes, to be sure, ven I inform her how ve've bin out with two real guns, and kill'd our own dinner. I'm bless'd if she'll swallow it!"

"I must say ve have seen a little life," said Grubb.

"And death too," added Spriggs. "Vitness the pig!"

"Now don't!" remonstrated Grubb, who was rather sore upon this part of the morning's adventures.

"And the gardener,"—persisted Spriggs.

"Hush for goodness sake!" said Mr. Richard, very seriously, "for if that 'ere affair gets vind, ve shall be blown, and—"

—In came the dinner. The display was admirable and very abundant, and the keen air, added to the unusual exercise of the morning, had given the young gentlemen a most voracious appetite.

The birds were particularly sweet, but afforded little more than a mouthful to each.

The 'wedgetables,' however, with a due proportion of fine old Cheshire, and bread at discretion, filled up the gaps. It was only marvellous where two such slender striplings could find room to stow away such an alarming quantity.

How calm and pleasant was the 'dozy feel' that followed upon mastication, as they opened their chests (and, if there ever was a necessity for such an action, it was upon this occasion,) and lolling back in their chairs, sipped the 'genuine malt and hops,' and picked their teeth!

The talkative Spriggs became taciturn. His gallantry, however, did prompt him, upon the production of a 'fresh pot,' to say,

"Vell, Grubbs, my boy, here's the gals!"

"The gals!" languidly echoed Mr. Richard, tossing off his tumbler, with a most appropriate smack.

CHAPTER VI.

The Reckoning.

"PULL the bell, Spriggs," said Mr. Richard, "and let's have the bill."

Mr. Augustus Spriggs obeyed, and the landlord appeared.

"Vot's to pay?"

"Send you the bill directly, gentlemen," replied the landlord, bowing, and trundling out of the room.

The cook presently entered, and laying the bill at Mr. Grubb's elbow, took off the remnants of the 'game,' and left the sportsmen to discuss the little account.

"My eye! if this ain't a rum un!" exclaimed Grubb, casting his dilating oculars over the slip.

"Vy, vot's the damage?" enquired Spriggs.

"Ten and fourpence."

"Ten and fourpence!—never!" cried his incredulous companion. "Vot a himposition."

"Vell!" said Mr. Grubb, with a bitter emphasis, "if this is finding our own wittles, we'll dine at the hor'nary next time"—

"Let's have a squint at it," said Mr. Spriggs, reaching across the table; but all his squinting made the bill no less, and he laid it down with a sigh. "It is coming it rayther strong, to be sure," continued he; "but I dare say it's all our happearance has as done it. He takes us for people o' consequence, and"—

"Vot consequence is that to us?" said Grubbs, doggedly.

"Vell, never mind, Dick, it's on'y vonce a-year, as the grotto-boys says—
"

"It need'nt to be; or I'll be shot if he mightn't vistle for the brads. Howsomever, there's a hole in another suv'rin."

"Ve shall get through it the sooner," replied the consoling Spriggs. "I see, Grubb, there aint a bit of the Frenchman about you"—

"Vy, pray?"

"Cos, you know, they're fond o' changing their suv'rins, and—you aint!"

The pleasant humour of Spriggs soon infected Grubb, and he resolved to be jolly, and keep up the fun, in spite of the exorbitant charge for the vegetable addenda to their supply of game.

"Come, don't look at the bill no more," advised Spriggs, but treat it as old Villiams does his servants ven they displeases him."

"How's that?"

"Vy, discharge it, to be sure," replied he.

This sage advice being promptly followed, the sportsmen, shouldering their guns, departed in quest of amusement. They had not, however, proceeded far on their way, before a heavy shower compelled them to take shelter under a hedge.

"Werry pleasant!" remarked Spriggs.

"Keep your powder dry," said Grubb.

"Leave me alone," replied Spriggs; "and I think as we'd better pop our guns under our coat-tails too, for these ere cocks aint vater-cocks, you know! Vell, I never seed sich a rain. I'm bless'd if it vont drive all the dickey-birds to their nestes."

"I vish I'd brought a numberella," said Grubbs.

"Lank! vot a pretty fellow you are for a sportsman!" said Spriggs, "it don't damp my hardour in the least. All veathers comes alike to me, as the butcher said ven he vos a slaughtering the sheep!"

Mr. Richard Grubb, here joined in the laugh of his good-humoured friend, whose unwearied tongue kept him in spirits—rather mixed indeed than neat—for the rain now poured down in a perfect torrent.

"I say, Dick," said Spriggs, "vy are ve two like razors?"

"Cos ve're good-tempered?"

"Werry good; but that aint it exactly—cos ve're two bright blades, vot has got a beautiful edge!"

"A hexcellent conundrum," exclaimed Grubb. "Vere do you get 'em?'

"All made out of my own head,—as the boy said ven be showed the wooden top-spoon to his father!"

CHAPTER VII.

A sudden Explosion—a hit by one of the
Sportsmen, which the other takes amiss.

A blustering wind arose, and like a burly coachman on mounting his box, took up the rain!

The two crouching friends taking advantage of the cessation in the storm, prepared to start. But in straightening the acute angles of their legs and arms, Mr. Sprigg's piece, by some entanglement in his protecting garb, went off, and the barrel striking Mr. Grubb upon the os nasi, stretched him bawling on the humid turf.

"O! Lord! I'm shot."

"O! my heye!" exclaimed the trembling Spriggs.

"O! my nose!" roared Grubb.

"Here's a go!"

"It's no go!—I'm a dead man!" blubbered Mr. Richard. Mr. Augustus Spriggs now raised his chum upon his legs, and was certainly rather alarmed at the sanguinary effusion.

"Vere's your hankercher?—here!—take mine,—that's it—there!—let's look at it."

"Can you see it?" said Grubb, mournfully twisting about his face most ludicrously, and trying at the same time to level his optics towards the damaged gnomon.

"Yes!"

"I can't feel it," said Grubb; "it's numbed like dead."

"My gun vent off quite by haccident, and if your nose is spoilt, can't you have a vax von?—Come, it ain't so bad!"

"A vax von, indeed!—who vouldn't rather have his own nose than all the vax vons in the vorld?" replied poor Richard. "I shall never be able to show my face."

"Vy not?—your face ain't touched, it's on'y your nose!"

"See, if I come out agin in an hurry," continued the wounded sportsman. "I've paid precious dear for a day's fun. The birds vill die a nat'ral death for me, I can tell you."

"It vos a terrible blow—certainly," said Spriggs; "but these things vill happen in the best riggle'ated families!"

"How can that be? there's no piece, in no quiet and respectable families as I ever seed!"

And with this very paradoxical dictum, Mr. Grubb trudged on, leading himself by the nose; Spriggs exerting all his eloquence to make him think lightly of what Grubb considered such a heavy affliction; for after all, although he had received a terrible contusion, there were no bones broken: of which Spriggs assured his friend and himself with a great deal of feeling!

Luckily the shades of evening concealed them from the too scrutinizing observation of the passengers they encountered on their return, for such accidents generally excite more ridicule than commiseration.

Spriggs having volunteered his services, saw Grubb safe home to his door in Tower Street, and placing the two guns in his hands, bade him a cordial farewell, promising to call and see after his nose on the morrow.

The following parody of a customary paragraph in the papers will be considered, we think, a most fitting conclusion to their day's sport.

"In consequence of a letter addressed to Mr. Augustus Spriggs, by Mr. Richard Grubb, the parties met early yesterday morning, but after firing several shots, we are sorry to state that they parted without coming to any satisfactory conclusion."